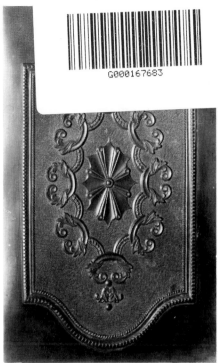

Decorative panels moulded in vulcanised rubber by Thomas Hancock shortly after 1843, when he filed the British patent for vulcanised rubber.

EARLY PLASTICS

Second edition

Sylvia Katz

Shire Publications Ltd

CONTENTS

Published in 1994 by Shire Publications Ltd, Cromwell House, Church Street, Princes Risborough, Buckinghamshire HP27 9AJ, UK. Copyright © 1986 and 1994 by Sylvia Katz. First edition 1986. Second edition 1994. Shire Album 168. ISBN 0 7478 0244 0.

Printed in Great Britain by CIT Printing Services, Press Buildings, Merlins Bridge, Haverfordwest, Dyfed SA61 1XF.

British Library Cataloguing in Publication Data: Katz, Sylvia. Early Plastics. 2 Rev. ed. – (Shire Albums; No. 168). I. Title. II. Series. 941. ISBN 0-7478-0244-0.

Cover: *Typical urea formaldehyde mouldings from the 1920s to the 1940s, including green Beetleware picnic cups and plates, Bandalasta box and plates, 1927-32, and a circular moulded box designed by Harry J. Earland in 1947.*

ACKNOWLEDGEMENTS
The author is very grateful for help and information from the following; Mr Carter, Telcon Plastics; Amanda Herries, the Museum of London; Richard de Peyer, Birmingham Museums and Art Gallery; Mr B. C. Whybrow, Thetford Moulded Products; Colin Williamson; and Gary Childs of Marlin Studios, for the extra photography. Photographs on the following pages are acknowledged to: BIP Limited, 20, 27, 28 (upper); Birmingham Museum and Art Gallery, 11 (lower), 12 (left), 13 (lower); David Bowsher, 11 (upper); British Telecom, 25 (upper); Catalogue of the Great Exhibition, 1851, 10 (upper left), 16 (lower); Design Council Archive, 5, 10 (upper right), 24 (right), 25 (lower), 28 (lower); Sylvia Katz and Gary Childs, Marlin Studios, 3, 6 (lower left), 12 (right), 13 (centre), 18 (upper), 21 (lower left), 22 (lower), 23, 29; Sylvia Katz and Fritz Curzon, cover, 22 (upper), 26; Sylvia Katz and Chris Smith, 18 (lower); Mary Metcalfe, 21 (centre); Museum of London, 6 (lower right), 8, 21 (lower right); Phaidon Press, 21 (upper); Rubber and Plastics Research Association, 16 (upper left); Science Museum, 1, 2, 6 (upper), 15 (upper), 16 (upper right and centre), 19, 24 (left); Victoria and Albert Museum, 9, 13 (upper left and right); Thetford Moulded Products, 10 (lower); John Topham Picture Library, 14, 15 (lower); Colin Williamson and Henning Christoph, 7 (lower).

Left: *A baked brick with bitumen mortar attached, found in the ruins of Babylon, 604-561 BC. The Babylonians used bitumen both as a mortar and as a road surface.*

Animal napkin rings made from sections of cast phenolic, sliced and polished, late 1930s to 1940s. Other typical uses for cast phenolic were umbrella handles, bracelets, candlesticks and lamp stands.

INTRODUCTION

It used to be generally believed that plastic was somehow a single material in different forms and colours. It was enough to say that something was 'made of plastic' without going into further detail, since any detail was assumed to be too technical for general understanding.

This is no longer sufficient. Progress in the development of twentieth-century materials, combined with a growing curiosity about our industrial past, means that it has become increasingly important to be able to identify materials.

Unlike the traditional technologies of metals, timber, glass and ceramics, plastics came on the scene very late, and their technology is developing daily. All the plastics in general use today are twentieth-century products, of which phenolic, for example Bakelite, was the first synthetic material, patented in 1907.

The foundations of the plastics industry, however, were laid in the nineteenth century, and this brief survey ends at the first synthetics, phenol formaldehyde and urea formaldehyde. Initially created as substitutes for expensive natural substances that were becoming scarce, and not necessarily as *cheaper* substitutes, plastics came into their own in the 1920s and 1930s, with a moment of glory during the Second World War. They subsequently fell into disrepute as a result of indiscriminate applications. Now at last they are accepted as an integral part of everyday experience, and as the history of plastics becomes clearer so 'plastic antiques' are being appreciated.

In 1901 Emil Fischer first conceived the idea that the chain-like molecular structure of natural plastics might be created synthetically. Around 1922 Hermann Staudinger postulated the unpopular idea that plastics were made up from extremely long chains of molecules; and finally in 1927, in the research laboratories of Du Pont, Wallace Carothers began his research into the analysis of the structure of plastics. The result of his work was a series of deliberately designed polymers.

THE CHEMISTRY OF PLASTICS

Plastics are materials that can be shaped during processing, and almost all of them contain organic polymers. Organic substances are those based on carbon, the element found in all living things. Materials such as clay and glass are also mouldable, but inorganic. Polymers are long chains of repeating molecular groups of chemicals known as monomers.

As the carbon atom possesses four arms, or valencies, it has the special ability to link up with other atoms to form molecules, and ultimately exceedingly long chains. Polythene, for example, consists of thousands of linked monomer units of ethylene. In the early days these monomers were derived from the distillation of coal, but now they come almost entirely from oil and natural gas.

The process of linking monomers to form polymers is known as polymerisation. An example of simple polymerisation is the creation of polyethylene (polythene for short) from units of ethylene:

$$\text{ethylene monomer unit:} \quad \begin{array}{c} \text{H} \quad \text{H} \\ | \quad \ | \\ \text{C} = \text{C} \\ | \quad \ | \\ \text{H} \quad \text{H} \end{array}$$

links up to become polyethylene:

$$\begin{array}{c} \text{H} \ \ \text{H} \ \ \text{H} \ \ \text{H} \ \ \text{H} \ \ \text{H} \\ | \ \ | \ \ | \ \ | \ \ | \ \ | \\ \text{—C—C—C—C—C—C—etc} \\ | \ \ | \ \ | \ \ | \ \ | \ \ | \\ \text{H} \ \ \text{H} \ \ \text{H} \ \ \text{H} \ \ \text{H} \ \ \text{H} \end{array}$$

There are a number of materials occurring in nature which fit into this definition, such as horn, bitumen, shellac and rubber. Others, such as celluloid and casein, are natural materials that have been modified by chemicals. The synthetic plastics are those made completely from man-made chemicals.

Plastics can be generally divided into two groups depending on how they react to heat: the thermoplastic and the thermosetting groups. Thermoplastic polymers, such as gutta-percha and celluloid, can be resoftened and remoulded many times. Thermosetting plastics are heated and moulded only once into an irreversible shape, because the molecules become cross-linked and locked into a three-dimensional grid.

Plastics can also be modified by additives which make them suited to different purposes. For example, fillers such as wood flour are added for strength and decoration; glass-fibre increases toughness.

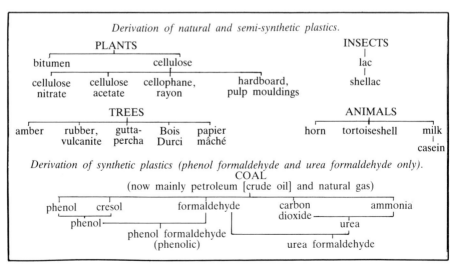

Derivation of natural and semi-synthetic plastics.

PLANTS — bitumen — cellulose
cellulose nitrate, cellulose acetate, cellophane, rayon, hardboard, pulp mouldings

INSECTS — lac — shellac

TREES — amber, rubber, vulcanite, gutta-percha, Bois Durci, papier mâché

ANIMALS — horn, tortoiseshell, milk — casein

Derivation of synthetic plastics (phenol formaldehyde and urea formaldehyde only).
COAL
(now mainly petroleum [crude oil] and natural gas)
phenol, cresol, formaldehyde, carbon dioxide, ammonia
phenol
phenol formaldehyde (phenolic)
urea
urea formaldehyde

Necklace, bracelet and earrings of carved amber scarabs set in silver. Designed by O. Shilling for I. G. Shwartz & Son, Copenhagen.

AMBER

Considering the definition of plastics as organic materials composed of long molecular chains with 'plastic' mouldable properties, it is surprising how many materials with this structure exist in nature. Amber is one of the oldest, usually thought of as a golden-hued resinoid, carved into objects such as beads and crucifixes. But amber is a thermoplastic resin which can be heated and moulded. It is a fossilised resin derived from trees that grew millions of years ago and was used by the ancient Greeks as a water-proof varnish. It ranges in colour from the palest yellow to almost black and was a constituent of the lacquer coating on nineteenth-century papier mâché.

Pressed amber is made from waste pieces heated and pressed together and can be distinguished by faint lines flowing through the resin in one direction.

Amber was one of the natural resins most imitated by cheaper plastics, particularly cast phenolic in the 1920s and 1930s.

BITUMEN

Bitumen is usually considered to be one of the earliest organic moulding materials and has often been described as a typical plastic. It is heat-softened and shaped in cold moulds, and it is sometimes heated afterwards to dry it out. Mixed with different fillers, it becomes suitable for a variety of applications.

Bitumen is a generic name for hydrocarbons formed within the earth from prehistoric vegetation. Its chief property is electrical resistance, and so most mouldings will be found in insulation applications. Hard rubber (vulcanite) was the first 'plastic' to be used for this in the nineteenth century, but by the end of the century bitumen had taken over many uses in Britain, with the expanding electrical industry one of the first to benefit.

Collecting and melting bitumen, from Agricola's 'De Re Metallica', Book II, 1556. Deposits of bitumen are found mainly in Trinidad and South America, and it can still be seen seeping through the walls of the Tar Tunnel at Coalport near Ironbridge, Shropshire.

HORN AND TORTOISESHELL

Hoof, horn and tortoiseshell are organic materials based on the protein keratin, and since prehistoric times they have been worked by man and heat-shaped like other thermoplastics.

Horn used to be cheap and plentiful, and the processes of heating, splitting and flattening it were simple. Drinking horns, shoe horns and combs use horn in its natural state,

Left: *A lacquered Thetford Pulp Ware powder bowl (upper) by Thetford Moulded Products, late nineteenth century, and a moulded bitumen bottle stopper (lower) with the remains of perished rubber, Batey and Company, 1920s. Bitumen saucepan and door handles and electrical fittings can still be found.*
Right: *Pressed horn box depicting 'The King's Champion' by John Obrisset, about 1710-20. Buffalo horn was used for most pressed decorated mouldings.*

Left: *Horn book with an alphabet and prayer, set in a leather-covered frame protected by a sheet of clear horn, eighteenth century. This was a one-page learning text used by young schoolchildren. The horn looks very like sheet celluloid.*
Right: *Lanthorn with panes of expensive glass replaced by clear sheets of pressed and scraped greenhorn, mid nineteenth century.*

perhaps with some simple heat shaping, but boxes, buttons and jewellery were shaped by being pressed into moulds. Cow, ox and buffalo horn and hoof become softened and plastic when heated, which was usually done over a fire. Sheffield boxes, popular from 1815 to 1855, and Victorian mourning jewellery are typical of this process. The density of pressed horn even allows pieces to be turned on a lathe for tool handles and seal boxes. The earliest horn mouldings recorded are the pressed medallions of John Osborn, an Englishman living in Amsterdam in the early seventeenth century, and the early eighteenth-century boxes of the celebrated John Obrisset.

Taking snuff became a social necessity in the eighteenth century, and snuffbox design reached its zenith at that time with horn the ideal material for moulding airtight boxes.

Typical late nineteenth-century brooches moulded in horn or hoof, with mother-of-pearl and metal inlay. The hand-shaped brooch shows the quality finish that could be achieved.

7

Many different materials attempted to imitate expensive tortoiseshell, including celluloid, casein and cellulose acetate. (Left) Mock tortoiseshell comb, probably celluloid. (Right) Hand-carved and shaped horn comb stained to imitate tortoiseshell. Both late nineteenth century.

A major industry was founded on the fashion for wearing haircombs in the nineteenth century, led by the French Empress Eugénie. Demand for combs increased until in 1860 the Empress switched to Spanish hairnets, and a whim of fashion nearly destroyed the livelihood of many horners, who were forced to diversify into snuffboxes. But the fashion returned and survived until the mid 1920s, although horn had by then been superseded by celluloid.

Tortoiseshell is an example of a com-pletely natural thermoplastic material and is one of the rare natural materials that cheaper synthetics and semi-synthetics have often attempted to emulate.

It is not easy to identify horn simulating tortoiseshell, but, whereas horn has a fibrous streaked structure, tortoiseshell can show a mottled ripple effect due to the annual growth of new plates. These layers can be separated and flattened into small pieces, and, unlike horn, thicker sections can be built up by pressing heated plates together.

Examples of pressed tortoiseshell from the late eighteenth century to the early nineteenth century, when pressed boxes were very popular. (Left to right) Patch/needle box, snuffbox, card case and etui, the two last finely inlaid with piqué work. (Below) Whist counters in a case.

8

Papier mâché parlour maid's tray inlaid with mother-of-pearl. English, about 1865.

PAPIER MÂCHÉ, PULP WARE AND BOIS DURCI

Papier mâché and pulp ware are not strictly plastics, but they are both examples of early mouldings based on cellulose, a natural substance with a long-chain molecular structure, and both rely on a curing process under heat and pressure to become infusible solids. The patented papier mâché process involved the heat-curing of glue, and pulp ware relied on a binder of natural resin and, later, of synthetic phenolic resin.

Henry Clay patented the papier mâché process in 1772 and set up a thriving business in Birmingham. Pulp made from finely ground wood flour or paper mixed with animal glue or gum arabic was pressed into a mould and dried out in an oven. The moulding was then sanded and polished, inlaid with decoration, painted or even decorated with a printed design, and finally japanned or lacquered. Another process, similar to the craft method of today, was to shape layers of damp paper over a mould. Many Victorian items were reinforced with metal

wire, but unfortunately large papier mâché objects have not survived very well and are now uncommon.

Mouldings were not very heat-proof, so virtually all applications are decorative: trays, spectacle cases, tea caddies, card cases, which were very popular around 1830, and the cheapest snuffboxes, which were made in large quantities between 1820 and 1860.

In England the Patent Pulp Manufacturing Company, now Thetford Moulded Products, began moulding pulp ware in 1879 'in imitation of leather, earthenware and papier mâché' and continued to do so into the 1940s. The pulp was made from purified ground wood and linseed oil and compressed into sieve-like formers and baked in ovens. Later phenolic resin was added with a top coat of melamine, producing a composition very similar to decorative laminates, such as Formica. Surfaces could be embossed or smooth, and after trimming the mouldings were coated with lacquer or japan. Pulp ware

9

Left: *At the Great Exhibition of 1851, Henry Clay & Company exhibited many papier mâché goods, including a dressing table inlaid with mother-of-pearl, and a chair and footstool to match. It is surprising to see such ambitious structures.*
Right: *Papier mâché chair with cane seat, inlaid with mother-of-pearl and decorated. English about 1810.*

possesses a certain 'plasticky' feel. Unlike papier mâché, mouldings were resistant to impact and hot water and they provided a cheap, lightweight alternative to ceramic mugs, jugs and bowls in the home. It can therefore be regarded as a forerunner of modern domestic plastics.

Bois Durci was another moulding material based on cellulose, patented in 1855 in Paris by Lepage. He intended it as a substitute for other natural materials such as 'wood, leather, bone, metal and other hard or plastic substances'. It was made from wood flour blended with blood and egg al-

General view of the Patent Pulp Manufacturing Company, about 1935, with presses, formers and untrimmed bowls.

10

The two main uses for pulp mouldings by the Patent Pulp Manufacturing Company were mining and pith helmets and roll-top baby baths, but a wide range of domestic products was also made.

bumen, and dried. When this mixture was placed in a mould and compressed in a heated hydraulic press it became a brown or black thermoset. The polished surface of the mould could give it a metallic or bronze-like finish, and the wood flour can often be seen quite clearly.

Bois Durci mouldings are now rare as they were made commercially only from the 1860s to 1875. Lepage moulded ink-wells, desk sets and picture frames, but plaques were extremely popular. These usually depicted royalty and other well-known people and were often screwed to furniture, such as pianos. The Pinto Collection in Birmingham Museum houses about thirty medallions.

The impress of a Bois Durci trademark sometimes found on the reverse of mouldings. Another mark was a small bird's wing, but many mouldings are unmarked. Late nineteenth century.

Left: *Bois Durci plaques showing the glossy finish and fine moulded detail possible with this material. These black mouldings were probably made from powdered ebony or rosewood. Late nineteenth century.*
Right: *Bronze-style sleeping Cupid paperweight showing contrasting surface textures of smooth and grained Bois Durci. Late nineteenth century.*

LAC AND SHELLAC

Many polymers were originally developed as coatings, and the earliest use of plastic-type lacquers can be traced back to the ancient Chinese, Japanese and Egyptians. Natural lac is tapped from the lacquer trees of east Asia and was described by Joseph Needham in 'An Early Medieval Chinese Alchemical Text on Aqueous Solutions' (*AMBIX* volume VII, number 3, 1959) as 'the most ancient industrial "plastic" known to man'.

Like some modern paint finishes, lac polymerises into a hard lacquer through atmospheric exposure, becoming tough enough to resist humidity and withstand boiling water. Chinese lacquer is, strictly, the carving of the build-up of very many layers of lacquer, often over a wooden frame.

Shellac is derived from the secretion of the *Coccus lacca* beetle larvae found in India and Malaya. Encrustations are collected by hand and melted into a brownish brittle resin, which is formed into flakes, sheets and rods. Thousands of years ago the Egyptians used shellac to coat their mummies, but it was not until it was discovered that it could be compounded with fillers that it became a tough, mouldable material.

This led to two important developments. The first was the pressing of sound records, which founded the record industry. The second was that the hydraulic presses used to mould the records formed the basis of future automatic production in plastics. Early shellac records were pressed from a mixture of powdered filler, such as slate, bound with shellac resin. The slate filler wore the steel needles down very quickly, but this was later solved by the development of vinyl microgroove records. Pre-First World War Edison records look like phenolic, but they have a core of shellac bound with wood flour and filler.

The pioneer shellac moulder was Samuel

Above: *Carved Chinese lacquer can look very 'plastic', like this sixteenth-century box carved in black and red marbled lacquer.*

Above right: *Cylindrical box of carved red lacquer prunus sprays over a metal base. Chinese, sixteenth century.*

Right: *Black shellac mirror (left) and hairbrush with finely moulded decoration of herons, bulrushes and water flowers. Marked 'Diatite', and patented 1868 and 1870. (Right) Dark brown shellac card case with silver clasp, late nineteenth century. From 1860 it was fashionable for ladies and gentlemen of distinction to leave visiting cards, and many card cases were moulded in early plastics such as papier mâché, shellac and vulcanite.*

Below: *Two shellac union cases (left and right) which once protected daguerreotypes and ambrotypes, the earliest types of photographic portraits. Union cases were patented by Samuel Peck in the United States in 1852. (Centre) Moulded Bois Durci plaque with woody appearance.*

13

Peck in the United States, who in the early 1850s started using shellac to mould union cases. These were velvet-lined, hinged frames for holding the early photographs known as daguerreotypes, which were very fragile, one-off collodion plates. Union cases are fine examples of nineteenth-century plastics mouldings. They were compression-moulded from a mixture of wood flour bound with shellac, which was capable of reproducing very fine detailing. Peck's best cases date from the 1860s, as do the cases of another American company, Littlefield, Parsons & Company.

Visiting cards were invented in 1860 and card cases gave shellac another use, but it has played a longer enduring part in the manufacture of hard and felt hats, for which it is still in use today. Bowler, top and riding hats all rely on shellac for their shape and hardness. Flakes of shellac are melted in boiling water and then soaked in ammonia to form a resin, into which pieces of twill are dipped. These are dried and cut to shape and pressed into wooden moulds with hot irons.

Bowler hats are made from rabbit fur stiffened with shellac. The basic shape is moulded first and, since shellac is thermoplastic, the hat can then be heated so that the resin softens and the shape can be finally adjusted to fit the individual head.

GUTTA-PERCHA

Gutta-percha is a completely natural plastic, and from the mid nineteenth century until the 1930s it was moulded into many domestic and industrial products. It is chemically similar to rubber but is a hard substance scraped by hand from the bark of Palaquium trees in Malaya, Borneo and Sumatra. Cleaned, kneaded and softened in hot water, it becomes a malleable plastic.

Gutta-percha can be thought of as an early type of polythene. Many of the objects it was moulded into, such as buckets, containers, tubing and toys, have been made in polythene for many years.

In 1843 samples of gutta-percha reached England in the shape of tool handles and small animal sculptures made by natives in Malaya. Michael Faraday identified its

Ornate inkstand moulded in gutta-percha by the Gutta Percha Company, about 1851. Gutta-percha was moulded into a great many products, ranging from boots, horseshoes, tables, mirrors and inkstands to matchboxes and even 'dumb jockeys' for training jockeys.

The following Gutta Percha Articles will be found of great value to Emigrants, especially such as are proceeding to the

GOLD DIGGINGS.

Gutta Percha
Lining
for Boxes.
Buckets.
Drinking
Mugs.
Life Buoys.
Flasks.
Gold Washing
Bowls.
Syphons.

Gutta Percha
Tubing.
Suctions
for Pumps.
Jugs.
Carboys for
Gunpowder.
Miners' Caps.
Soles for
Boots & Shoes.

Above: *Examples of gutta-percha mouldings from a nineteenth-century catalogue. All these types of objects would now be moulded in modern synthetics.*
Right: *A shovel being shaped by hand in gutta-percha, with a gutta-percha jug in the background, and a chemical bottle in the foreground. Gutta-percha was ideal for making acid-proof bottles and buckets.*

excellent insulating properties, and its acid resistance made it immediately suitable for the expanding photographic industry. In 1845 the Gutta Percha Company was established in London, and its first major commission was to insulate the submarine telegraphic link planned between England and France. Following its success, the company, now Telcon Plastics, continued unrivalled to insulate submarine telegraph cables for nearly one hundred years.

Bewley designed the first extrusion machine in 1845, and gutta-percha was one of the first plastics to be extruded. All kinds of tubing were extruded, as were lengths of imitation wood mouldings for panels and friezes, almost identical to modern foamed polyurethane designs. Few gutta-percha mouldings are to be found now, but a small collection can be seen at Telcon Plastics in Kent.

15

Above left: *Native moulding in unvulcanised natural rubber from South America, about 1851.*

Above right: *Replica of the first pneumatic rubber tyre patented by Robert William Thomson in 1845. He had hoped it would be used on the wheels of trains and bath chairs, but rubber was not generally available at that time and it was not until Dunlop's patent of 1888 that vulcanised rubber revolutionised the motor industry.*

Left: *Child's ball made of natural rubber latex. Rubber was first seen by Europeans when Christopher Columbus found children playing with bouncing balls and moulded toys in Haiti in the late fifteenth century.*

Below: *Lieutenant Halkett's india-rubber cloak boat, exhibited at the Great Exhibition of 1851, was a very functional item of clothing. Inflated with bellows (B) carried in the pocket, it became a boat suitable for hunters and travellers.*

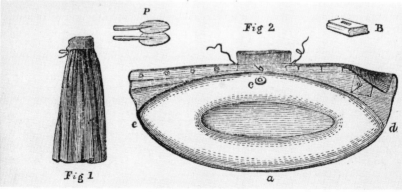

Vulcanite chatelaines for carrying accessories such as scissors, pincushions and notebooks, nineteenth century. During the period of Queen Victoria's mourning for the Prince Consort, which lasted from 1861 until 1887, early plastics such as vulcanite, celluloid and casein were ideal as black alternatives to expensive horn and jet.

HARD RUBBER, VULCANITE AND EBONITE

Rubber was the first natural polymer to be chemically altered by man, and its processing technology, with those of gutta-percha and shellac, established the designs of modern plastics machinery.

Rubber in the form of latex has been collected for centuries from Brazilian trees. It reached Europe in 1736, when its erasing properties were soon put to use, but it remained of little practical use, too rigid in cold temperatures, too sticky in hot, and it perished too quickly. In solution it was used as a waterproof coating, and Macintosh sandwiched the sticky gum between layers of heavy cotton to make his famous raincoats.

In 1839 an American dealer in agricultural tools, Charles Goodyear, discovered the final clue to making rubber of lasting value: vulcanisation. If rubber is compounded with sulphur, a remarkable change in properties occurs: not only can the rubber be moulded into shapes that are unaffected by changes in temperature, but the mouldings seem to possess a rubbery, resilient property. In the process of vulcanisation, the long chains of rubber molecules are prevented from slipping again during heating by cross-links, and the polymer is set in its moulded form. Different degrees of resilience can be achieved by varying the amount of added sulphur. Goodyear had created the first thermoset. In Britain, Thomas Hancock developed the concept of vulcanisation much further and established the first rubber industry, producing boots, hoses, coach springs and elastic bands.

Rubber vulcanised with 25 to 50 per cent sulphur becomes an extremely hard substance known as hard rubber, vulcanite or ebonite, as it resembles ebony. It offers many advantages, in particular chemical and heat resistance, and was moulded into pumps and valves, photographic equipment, buckets, battery boxes, pipe stems and telephones.

One of the immediate uses for vulcanite was to relieve denture wearers of the discomfort of ivory or bone dentures. Dentures were patented by the Goodyear Rubber Company in 1840, and vulcanite remained the standard material for over seventy years. Although always dark in colour, it could be heavily pigmented to pass for gums and was applied as a facing over a base of darker rubber.

17

Left: *Smoking accessories were often moulded in vulcanite, such as these pipe stems (top). The vesta matchbox (centre) has a Jubilee portrait of Queen Victoria, about 1897, and each end of the box is fixed with a spring hinge. Fountain pens and propelling pencils such as these are still easy to find; these pens date from about 1915, and the orange and black mottled pencil, from the Staveley Coal and Iron company, from the 1930s.*

Below: *Parkesine mouldings, 1861-8, inlaid with silver and mother-of-pearl: (left) box lid; (right) two book covers. Parkes experimented with piqué work, embossing, painting and mixing colours to create attractive patterns.*

Parkesine hair clasp, moulded, carved and inlaid with mother-of-pearl.

PARKESINE AND CELLULOID

Vulcanite was the first commercially important plastic. The second was celluloid, also semi-synthetic, but commercialised domestically on a much larger scale.

Alexander Parkes, a Birmingham inventor, formulated a mouldable dough by modifying cotton fibres with nitric and sulphuric acids and plasticising it with oils and camphor. On heating, this dough became plastic and could be pressed into moulds or shaped by hand. The material was known as Parkesine and was presented at the Great International Exhibition of 1862 as an acknowledged innovation. Unfortunately, Parkes's company suffered badly as customers returned warped and cracked mouldings. Parkes lost control of his company and his friend Daniel Spill took over.

Simultaneously in America the Hyatt brothers had also been experimenting with a similar substance but had solved the problem of the correct use of camphor. They patented celluloid in 1869, and in England Spill began to manufacture it using the tradenames Xylonite and Ivoride.

Sheet celluloid is made by extruding cellulose nitrate dough into lengths, which are laid together and heat-pressed into homogeneous blocks. The blocks are planed into thin sheets, which are dried and flattened for moulding. Colouring was done by hand with dyes, or coloured chips were mixed into a base colour to form a block for slicing. Several layers pressed together built up a depth of colour, and pearl effects could also be created with additives such as mica particles.

Despite its flammability, celluloid's greatest achievement has been in the film industry, both as cine film and as the 'cels' for creating animated films. In addition, it made photography available to many people. Even after non-flammable cellulose acetate film was developed in the early 1930s celluloid was still considered superior and it was used in the United States up to 1952. Unfortunately celluloid film is now disintegrating fast, attacked by its own nitric acid fumes.

Other major uses for celluloid included toys, haircombs, dressing-table accessories and table-tennis balls – no other modern plastic has succeeded in creating the special, light bounce of celluloid.

Above: *A sheet of Xylonite (celluloid) being planed off a block.*

Below: *Planed celluloid 'hides' seasoning in hot air in order to evaporate the camphor before moulding. Celluloid is inflammable with a 10.8 to 11.2 per cent content of nitrogen, although some types of celluloid, such as cine film, were more inflammable than others.*

Right: *Celluloid could simulate expensive shell very convincingly. This vacuum-formed hairpin box, with plated hinge, catch and label, is marked 'Antwerp 1888' and has 'Deposée' stamped into it.*

Below: *Carving knife with moulded celluloid handle.*

Below left: *Celluloid provided a cheap alternative to ivory. The two prayer books were each made with three sheets of celluloid, one (right) with a silver cross hallmarked 1935; the other (left), unlike real ivory, shows the faint lines often typical of celluloid sheet. The flower brooch (lower right) was moulded and then carved. The crucifix was made from hollow celluloid mouldings in the 1890s and looks very 'plasticky'.*

Below right: *Celluloid Kewpie doll, moulded in the United States in 1912-13. It is typical of vacuum-formed cellulose nitrate toys, with moulded sections cemented together.*

Above: *Dressing-table plastics typical of the ivory and pearlised types of celluloid. The powder and pill boxes have vacuum-formed lids, and the brush and mirror backs were made by stamping and moulding blanks, then cementing them round wooden frames. Most of these items were moulded by Halex between the 1890s and the 1940s.*

Below: *Rolinx 'exploding' cigarette box (right), moulded in cellulose acetate with simulated leather, 1950s. As the shutter is rolled back, the cigarette holders appear and fan out like a hand. The pink streamlined butter dish (left) was moulded in cellulose acetate in the 1950s.*

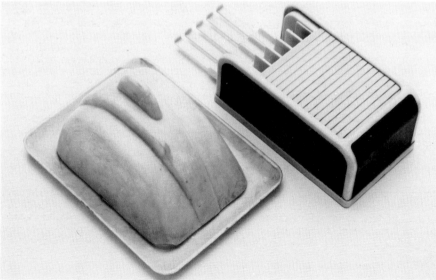

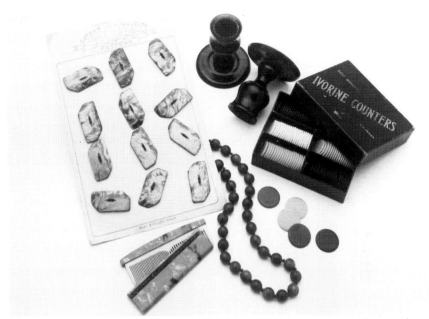

Casein has many visual similarities with celluloid, particularly its range of colours and patterns. The picture shows Tortoisene candlesticks with vulcanite liners, Ivorine counters, a celluloid comb and a sheet of casein buttons. Buttons often developed a crazed surface due to water absorption.

CELLULOSE ACETATE

Almost as soon as cellulose nitrate appeared on the market in the late 1860s, attempts began to reduce its flammability, but it was not until after 1905 that fibres and films were made in America by treating pure cellulose cotton with acetic anhydride, instead of nitric acid.

By the start of the First World War cellulose acetate had shown itself ideal as non-flammable dope for waterproofing aircraft fabric. At the end of the war the Dreyfus brothers converted the spare capacity to rayon, a cellulose acetate 'plastics' fibre. Finally, in 1927 cellulose acetate was compounded into a dough which could be rolled into blocks or extruded into profiled lengths.

Compression-moulded thermosets such as phenolic and urea formaldehyde had been developed, but cellulose acetate was a thermoplastic and unsuitable for the thermoset moulding processes. In 1926 Eckert and Ziegler designed the first horizontal injection moulding machine, which could inject about 2 ounces (57 grams) of plastic and was ideal for using up cellulose acetate. For twenty years cellulose acetate was the only colourful thermoplastic for general injection moulding until the arrival of polythene and polystyrene at the end of the Second World War.

CASEIN

Although of minor importance, casein is an early moulding material based on a natural animal product, skim milk. Casein is the protein found in milk and consists of long, polymer-like chains of molecules. When milk is treated with acid it separates into curds and whey. Dried and powdered curds were mixed into a dough and extruded into lengths, which were hardened in formaldehyde, a process which took days, or even weeks, depending on the thickness of the extrusion. This hardened the material by

Left: *Calling dial by the Automatic Electric Company, Chicago, about 1906. Parts of early telephones with separate transmitters and receivers were moulded in vulcanite before phenolic (Bakelite) took over.*
Right: *Hairdryer made by GEC in 1937. This lethal-looking machine is moulded inappropriately in walnut-effect phenolic. Reinforced with various fillers, phenolic possesses excellent mechanical strength and electrical resistance and was moulded into many heat-resistant components such as plugs and fuses, saucepan handles and ashtrays.*

cross-linking before machining and polishing.

Casein was first patented as Galalith by Spitteler and Krische in Germany in 1899, and a similar material, Erinoid, was patented in England in 1909. As with celluloid, virtually any colour could be achieved, as well as natural effects such as ivory, tortoiseshell and pearl, and it was moulded into similar products such as gaming chips, dice, candlesticks and spoons. By far the greatest amount was used decoratively as buttons, buckles and hairgrips.

PHENOL FORMALDEHYDE (PHENOLIC)

Phenol formaldehyde was the first totally man-made plastic and is far better known by its tradename, 'Bakelite', although there are many other tradenames for this material. Phenolic is a thermosetting plastic made by reacting phenol (carbolic acid) with formaldehyde, a product of carbon monoxide and hydrogen. Phenolic resin is brittle, but with fillers of cotton flock, wood flour, paper or fabric it can be moulded into countless useful objects.

The reaction of phenol with formaldehyde had been known about since the 1870s, but it was not until Leo Baekeland in the United States looked at it in a different way that the problems of polymerisation were overcome. His first 'heat and pressure' patent registered the new resin in 1907.

Phenolic mouldings are generally the easiest to identify. Colours are always limited to dark shades of brown, red, blue or green, often with the familiar mottled effect created by flakes of different colours. Sometimes the filler can be seen, or the

Siemens Neophone Number 162, 1929, introduced as the first handset micro telephone in phenolic. The address drawer contains a sheet of celluloid. This design was the largest ever order for Bakelite Limited and helped to promote the quick acceptance of the handset telephone.

laminated fabric.

Cast phenolic is an unfilled type of phenolic resin and therefore used mainly for decorative mouldings, particularly in the 1930s. Two or three colours skilfully blended could simulate the swirling patterns of natu-

Left: *Ekco AD 65 radio designed by Wells Coates for E. K. Cole, 1934. This was the first circular wireless, compression-moulded in phenolic resin.*
Right: *Quicklo revolving and detachable phenolic desk tray set by J. Cook, 1935. This was produced in 'medium oak' or 'ebony black'.*

ral products such as amber, marble or onyx. The material is not stable in large, thick sections as it tends to craze internally, and the largest mouldings appear to be Ameri-can radios of the 1930s and 1940s, such as those made by FADA or Addison from slabs of bright, solid colour.

Examples of phenolic mouldings, including a revolving 'Smoker's Friend', 1930s (left), an electric bedwarmer bottle, 1947 (right), and a Bush television set, 1949. The lamp has a tasselled celluloid shade.

Part of the Bandalasta Ware 'Morning Tea Set', compression-moulded in alabaster-effect urea formaldehyde by Brookes & Adams, late 1920s.

UREA FORMALDEHYDE

By the 1920s phenol formaldehyde was well established, but what was needed was another all-purpose thermosetting plastic, with good electrical resistance, but offering a lighter range of colours.

In 1924 Edmund Rossiter at British Cyanides experimented in substituting thiourea for phenol in the reaction with formaldehyde and succeeded in making the first light-coloured moulding powder, which was unveiled at the Wembley Exhibition of 1925. The plastic soon appeared in the form of delicately mottled domestic mouldings.

Around the same time, an improved version, urea formaldehyde, was commercialised by British Cyanides under the trade name Beetle, and Beetleware became a household name. Urea formaldehyde brought a clean, hygienic look to electrical products such as hairdryers, shavers and plugs and as a resin had many important applications. The impregnation of kraft paper made possible coloured decorative laminates suitable for the surfaces of modern hotel bars, kitchens and offices.

The first part of the plastics story ends here with the 'poly' era about to begin. Polystyrene was developed by the Germans in 1929; unsaturated polyester resins were patented in 1933; ICI discovered polythene in 1933 and polymethyl methacrylate (acrylic) in 1934; the modern extruder for thermoplastics was designed by Troester in 1935; polyurethanes and PVC were first produced in 1937; and nylon, the first completely synthetic fibre, revolutionised the plastics world in 1938.

In the Second World War plastics had the opportunity to prove that they were no longer ersatz materials, and afterwards many of these plastics were released for general use. Without them our lives would be quite different, and much the poorer.

Bandalasta

Left: *A page from a Bandalasta Ware catalogue, 1927-32, showing pieces moulded in urea thiourea formaldehyde by Brookes & Adams. This was one of the most beautiful ranges of plastic tableware ever produced. If the catalogue had not described self-feeding cigarette caskets, toilet-roll holders and door plates the full range might never have been known about.*

Below: *The urea formaldehyde Beetleware cruet set was one of the best-known and most ubiquitous domestic mouldings. (Back) The obelisk-shaped prewar set with 'Odeon' style moulding. (Front) The rounded forms of the postwar 1946 version, designed by A. H. Woodfull at BIP Limited.*

BRIEF GUIDE TO IDENTIFICATION

PATENT NUMBERS, TRADE MARKS AND REGISTERED DESIGN NUMBERS

These numbers and marks provide a kind of hallmarking system and are the first obvious clues to look for. The Patent Office in London holds directories of all patent numbers and trade marks, the Register of Design Numbers is held at the Designs Registry, High Holborn, and detailed information about patented designs before 1909 is stored at the Public Record Office, Kew.

APPEARANCE

It is only by handling different plastics that their differences can be understood. Unfortunately it is not always so simple: for example, there are at least six natural and synthetic materials capable of simulating jet, and most of these can also imitate other materials.

HEAT TEST (PYROLYSIS)

A simple test will first determine whether the material is a thermoplastic or a thermoset. A hot pin is applied to a hidden part: if the material stays hard, it is a thermoset; if it yields, it is a thermoplastic. A whiff of chemicals may also be detected at the same time, but the following test is more thorough.

This test must always be done on a flame-proof surface, testing small pieces of plastic. Fumes must never be inhaled but sniffed carefully after the flame is extinguished. If you are uncertain, a professional chemist can be consulted. With a sharp knife, scrape off a small amount of powder from an unseen part on to a saucer and light carefully with a gas flame.

Amber: a hot pin goes in easily, but proper tests should be done professionally.

Bois Durci: no tests are available, but it usually has a woody, bronze or ebony colour and can look grainy because of the wood flour in the material.

Casein: when heated smells like burnt milk or cheese, revealing its milky origin.

Celluloid: often shows processing lines. When it is rubbed, the faint smell of camphor may be caught, and when burnt it 'pops' with a sooty flame, usually giving off a smell of camphor and nitric acid.

Cellulose acetate: when burnt, 'pops' like celluloid with little explosions, but smells of vinegar.

Papier mâché: feels organic and hollow and is warm to the touch. Sometimes reinforcing wire can be seen in broken parts.

Parkesine: rather cool to the touch, like ceramic, and can give off a faint smell of camphor.

Phenolic: very slow to burn. Has a yellow flame and gives off the scent of burning wood (the filler) and carbolic acid (phenol).

Pressed horn: has a hollow feel and often a cracked, fibrous surface. When burnt, it smoulders, and the keratin smells like burnt hair.

Shellac: a hot pin goes straight in, and when it is burnt there is a slight smell of sealing wax.

Tortoiseshell: has a natural, irregular grain. It burns with a flame and the keratin smells like burnt hair.

Urea formaldehyde: burns with no flame and with a fish-like odour.

Vulcanite: smells of sulphur and is often faded with a yellow tinge.

Typical urea formaldehyde mouldings. Two vacuum flasks by Thermos (1925) Limited: (right) 1930 model; (left) late 1940s version. Two Quickmix egg-flip mixers, 1949, and a yellow sugar shaker, late 1930s.

GUIDES TO IDENTIFICATION
Conservation of Plastics by John Morgan. The Plastics Historical Society and the Museums and Galleries Commission, 1991.
Simple Methods for the Identification of Plastics by D. Braun. Carl Hanser Verlag, Munich, 1982. Available from the Institute of Materials.

PROFESSIONAL TESTING
Commonwealth Mycological Institute, Culture Collection and Industrial Services, Ferry Lane, Richmond, Surrey TW9 3AF. Telephone: 081-940 4086.
Fulmer Yarsley Ltd, Trowers Way, Redhill, Surrey RH1 2JN. Telephone: 0737 965070.
Plastics Historical Society, 11 Hobart Place, London SW1W 0HL.
RAPRA Technology Ltd, Shawbury, Shrewsbury, Shropshire SY4 4NR. Telephone: 0939 250383.

CARE AND REPAIR

Early plastics should be cleaned very carefully. Start by wiping with a damp cloth and buff dry. Never use abrasive cleaners, but metal polish gives a pleasant sheen to many plastics. Here is a brief guide to cleaning some early plastic materials.

Amber, Bois Durci, celluloid: wipe and buff dry.
Casein, shellac: wipe with a soapy cloth and dry. A little metal polish or furniture cream gives lustre.
Horn: wipe with lukewarm distilled water and plain soap. Dry and apply wax cream polish or neatsfoot oil.
Papier mâché and pulp mouldings: wipe with a soapy cloth and polish with a little furniture cream.
Phenolic (Bakelite type plastics): a soapy wash is possible, using a toothbrush to clean out crevices. Dry and try an aerosol or metal polish.
Urea formaldehyde: can be washed in mild soapy water and buffed dry.

Vulcanite: clean with light mineral oil and buff.

Storage is a major problem with early plastic mouldings, which must never stand in direct sunlight or near hot lights as they may fade or crack. Store them in a cool, well ventilated place. This is particularly important with celluloid, which continues to give off fumes of nitric acid and camphor. If these fumes cannot escape, they can destroy the mouldings, and degrading objects must always be isolated as fumes can affect other celluloid objects. Celluloid, however, is not as explosive as some believe it to be.

Epoxy glues, such as Araldite, are suitable for repairing broken parts on most plastics, including horn, but use thinly as they tend to yellow with age. Celluloid becomes delicate with age, and to date epoxy glues are some of the least invasive to use for repair.

GLOSSARY

(Italics denote words cross-referenced in the glossary.)

Blow moulding: a process for moulding *thermoplastics* into hollow objects such as dolls and bottles by blowing air into a short tube of heated plastic, which expands to fill the interior of the mould.
Cold moulding: the moulding of plastics under pressure at room temperature, often with heat-curing.
Compression moulding: a process for moulding *thermosetting* plastics into radio cabinets, ash trays, plugs etc. A measured amount of plastic is placed in a heated steel mould, the top part of the mould closes over it, and heat and pressure force the plastic to flow in the cavity.
Cross-linking: the formation of chemical links between chains of molecules, which prevent the chains from slipping again during reheating.
Curing: the creation of a *polymer* through *polymerisation* and/or *cross-linking*.

Ebonite: see *vulcanite*.

Extrusion: the process for moulding continuous lengths of tubing, rod, film and profiles.

Formaldehyde: a colourless gas which, as a solution, reacts with *phenol* to make phenol formaldehyde, and with *urea* to make urea formaldehyde.

Injection moulding: a process formerly used only with *thermoplastics*, whereby softened plastic is forced along inside a metal cylinder by a screw. The screw stops and plunges molten plastic into a cold mould. Greater speed is possible than with *compression moulding*, and the join line of the mould, or the remains of the *sprue*, can usually be seen.

Lamination: a method of making strong sheets of plastic by compressing thermoset-impregnated paper or fabric between steel plates.

Molecule: the smallest possible unit of a chemical substance, composed of a group of atoms.

Monomer: the building block for making a plastic material. A compound which during *polymerisation* links up with other *molecules* to form very long chains, or *polymers*.

Phenol: also called carbolic acid, it reacts with *formaldehyde* to make phenol formaldehyde.

Plasticiser: a chemical additive that makes a *polymer* more flexible and mouldable.

Polymer: all polymers are plastics which have been made by the *polymerisation* of *monomers*.

Polymerisation: the process whereby small *molecules* are linked together to form giant molecules.

Semi-synthetic plastics: plastics made from natural materials treated with chemicals.

Sprue: in injection moulding, the channel through which the molten plastic is injected into the mould cavity. Also refers to the piece of hardened plastic left there, which is broken off.

Thermoplastics: plastics which can be heated and reshaped many times, for example celluloid and horn.

Thermosetting plastics: plastics which can be heated and moulded only once, as their molecules *cross-link*. Ideal therefore for making heat-resistant components such as plugs and handles.

Urea: colourless synthetic chemical made from ammonia and carbon dioxide, and used for making light-coloured urea formaldehyde mouldings.

Vulcanisation: a chemical reaction in which sulphur is used to cause *cross-linking* in rubber, making moulded shapes possible.

Vulcanite, ebonite: called hard rubber in the United States. An extremely hard *thermosetting* rubber, in which the *vulcanisation* process has been taken to the extreme.

FURTHER READING

BIP Ltd. *The Beetle Bulletin Guide To Plastics Antiques* (reprints from Beetle Bulletin numbers 30, 32 and 34). BIP Ltd, 1976.

Boymans-van Beuningen Museum, Rotterdam. *Bakeliet: Techniek, Vormgeving, Gebruik* (Bakelite: Technique, Form, Material) (catalogue). 1981.

The British Plastics Federation. *The World of Plastics*. 1986.

DiNoto, Andrea. *Art Plastic*. Abbeville Press, 1984.

Friedel, Robert. *Pioneer Plastic*. University of Wisconsin Press, 1983.

Hardwick, Paula. *Discovering Horn*. Lutterworth Press, 1981.

ICI Ltd. *Landmarks in the Plastics Industry 1862-1962*. 1962.

Katz, Sylvia. *Plastics: Designs and Materials*. Studio Vista, 1978.

Katz, Sylvia. *Classic Plastics*. Thames & Hudson, 1984.

Kaufman, Morris. *The First Century of Plastics*. Plastics and Rubber Institute, 1963.

Kölsch, Ulrich and Ursula. *Kunststoff Objekte 1860-1960* (Plastic Objects) (catalogue of touring exhibition). 1984.

Merriam, John. *Pioneering in Plastics*. East Anglian Magazine Ltd, 1976.

Muller, Helen. *Jet Jewellery and Ornaments*. Shire Publications, 1980.

Newport, Roger. *Plastic Antiques* (catalogue of travelling exhibition sponsored by BIP Ltd and Wolverhampton Polytechnic). 1976.

Pinto, Edward and Eva. *Tunbridge and Scottish Souvenir Ware*. G. Bell & Sons, 1970.

Rabolini, Anna. *Gli Anni di Plastica*. Gruppo Montedison, 1983.

Roudillon, Michel. *Bakelite*. Galerie Loft, 1982.

Telcon Plastics Ltd. *The Telcon Story 1850-1950*. Telcon Plastics Ltd, 1950.

SOURCES OF INFORMATION

The British Plastics Federation (BPF), 6 Bath Place, Rivington Street, London EC2A 3JE. Telephone: 071-457 5000. Publishes *The World of Plastics* softback and Factsheets on aspects of modern plastics.

Design Council Slide Loan Collection, 28 Haymarket, London SW1Y 4SU. Telephone: 071-839 8000. Slides from the Plastics Antiques Exhibition (1977) are available on loan.

Designs Registry, The Patent Office, 25 Southampton Buildings, London WC2A 1AY. Telephone: 071-438 4700. The Register of Design Numbers can be consulted.

The Plastics Historical Society (PHS), 11 Hobart Place, London SW1W 0HL. Write to the Honorary Secretary.

The Plastics Historical Society Library, The Mansion House, Ford, Shrewsbury, Shropshire SY5 9LZ. Telephone: 0743 850267.

Polymer Industry Education Centre (PIEC), University of York, Heslington, York. Telephone: 0904 432560.

Polymer Science Library, London School of Polymer Technology, Holloway Road, London N7 8DB. Telephone: 071-753 5128.

Public Record Office, Ruskin Avenue, Kew, Richmond, Surrey. Telephone: 081-876 3444. Pre-1909 patent information.

PLACES TO VISIT

To see those collections denoted by an asterisk, an appointment must be made in advance. Intending visitors to other museums are advised to find out the opening times before making a special journey.

Birmingham Museum and Art Gallery, Chamberlain Square, Birmingham B3 3DH. Telephone: 021-235 2834. The Pinto Collection* is an important collection of Bois Durci, but not on general display.

The Museum of London, 150 London Wall, London EC2Y 5HN. Telephone: 071-600 3699. The Worshipful Company of Horners Collection* is not on general display.

The Plastics Historical Society (PHS), Institute of Materials, 11 Hobart Place, London SW1W 0HL. Telephone: 071-245 9555 (Tuesdays). Collection of early plastics*, especially Parkesine.

The Science Museum, Exhibition Road, South Kensington, London SW7 2DD. Telephone: 071-598 3456. Plastics Gallery includes Parkesine, Ivoride, other early plastics, a Bakelite coffin, machinery and documentation.

Vestry House Museum, Vestry Road, London E17 9NH. Telephone: 081-509 1917. A local museum with a special Xylonite archive.